# Trucks and Diggers

by Gabby Goldsack

Copyright © **ticktock** Entertainment Ltd 2004

First published in Great Britain in 2004 by **ticktock** Media Ltd.,
Unit 2, Orchard Business Centre, North Farm Road, Tunbridge Wells, Kent, TN2 3XF

We would like to thank: Meme Ltd.
**Picture Credits:** Mack Trucks 4, 5. Peterbuilt Trucks 4, 5, 14, 22, 27. Saab Scania 8. New Holland Ltd.10–13.

ISBN 1 86007 444 8 HB
ISBN 1 86007 440 5 PB

Printed in China

# Contents

# Learning Advice

This book is designed to be both stimulating and accessible to young readers. Young children can show a wide range in ability. This is not necessarily a guide to later levels of achievement. Young children learn well through sharing. Therefore, all the activities in this book should be treated as an opportunity to share and talk about the pictures on each page. At this age, all reading should be shared reading. By showing a child that you find reading exciting, you will pass this positive image on to your child. Try to involve your child in each story as much as possible, ask and answer questions, and talk about any ideas that arise. Encourage your child to come up with ideas on his or her own. Many books on trucks and diggers are available at your local library.

# Trucks and Diggers:
## Trucks at Work

**There are many different types of trucks.** Some trucks help people who are building roads. Others carry food or petrol. There are even trucks that carries other trucks.

This **refuse truck** picks up rubbish and then takes it to the tip to help keep our cities clean.

The **heavy loader** truck is powerful, but it cannot go very fast with its huge load on board.

cab

grill

This truck is called a cement mixer. The truck stores cement and mixes it as it drives along. The whole back spins around slowly.

The back of the **tipper truck** lifts up to let the load slide out.

lights

# Truck Words

Can you find these words on the page?

lights

refuse truck

heavy loader

cab

tipper truck

cement mixer

grill

# Trucks and Diggers:
## Diggers at Work

**Diggers work on building sites.** A digger can lift and push earth around by using its arm and bucket. Some diggers have wheels and some have tracks.

bucket

This digger is called an **earth mover**. It has bigger wheels than any car. It carries tons of earth in its enormous bucket.

The tracks on this **bulldozer** help it grip as it pushes huge piles of earth.

tracks

arms

This **digger** has two arms. The bucket on the back digs holes, while the shovel on the front scoops and lifts dirt.

tyre

This **dumper truck** is so big that it is not allowed to travel on some roads. Trucks like these are used to move enormous loads of rock, earth, or coal.

# Digger Words

Can you find these words on the page?

bucket

earth mover

bulldozer

dumper truck

tyre

digger

arms

# Word Puzzles

**Look at these truck and digger pictures.**
Can you tell what order the words should go in?

1

truck

big

The

red

is

## Truck and Digger Words

**You have seen these words before.** Use the pictures to help you say them.

tyre

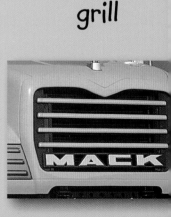

grill

**2**

can

digger

I

the

see

cold

snow

The

is

**3**

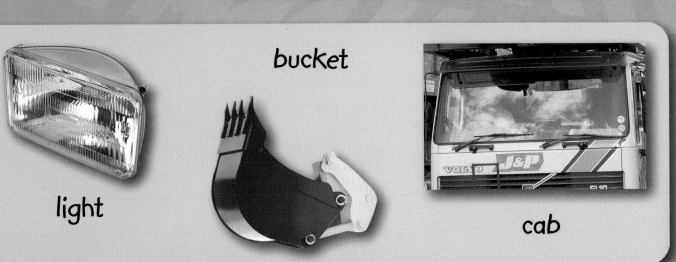

bucket

light

cab

**Word Puzzles answers: 1.** The big truck is red. **2.** I can see the digger. **3.** The snow is cold.

**9**

# A Story to Read:
## The Very Useful Tractor

This is **Bill the farmer**.

His tractor is bright **blue**.

The engine rumbles loudly

as the tractor ploughs the field.

Farmer Bill is in his tractor. He sees his farmer friend and gives him a wave.

Farmer Bill's tractor is always moving. Look at it go!

This tractor can do many jobs. It pushes dirt and ploughs the fields.

This giant combine harvester is cutting the **grain**. The farmer wants to cut the grain before it rains.

The grain is tipped into the trailer. What a heavy load! The tractor tows the trailer along the winding road.

Next, the tractor gathers **hay**. The hay is saved for the animals to eat in colder weather.

It is getting dark. Time to park the tractor in the shed.

**Can you answer these questions about the story you have just read?**

1 Who is driving the tractor?
2 What colour is the tractor?
3 What does the combine harvester cut?

# A Story to Share:
## Carl's Busy Day

Can you say the words in **bold**? Use the pictures to help you.

Carl drives a car transporter that delivers **cars** to people. Carl thinks that delivering cars is fun, but he wonders what it would be like to have another job.

Carl's first stop is the shipyard. Creeeeeak! goes the **crane** as it lifts a car onto the ship.

*Driving a crane could be fun*, thinks Carl.

Carl's next stop is the quarry. *Honk! Honk!* toots the horn of a **low loader** as it drives past. It is carrying a load of heavy rocks.

*Driving a low loader could be fun,* thinks Carl.

At the quarry, Carl unloads a new car for the supervisor. Nearby, a **dumper truck** unloads a mountain of dusty dirt.

*Driving a dumper truck could be fun,* thinks Carl.

Next, there
are new cars
to deliver to
the garage.
Wow, says Carl
when he sees a
**gasoline tanker**. The
license plate on the tanker show
that the driver has come a long way.

*Driving a gasoline tanker could be fun*, thinks Car

Carl sees a **truck** fly
past. *Tooooooooot!* goes
the truck. The driver is
in a hurry because
he needs to deliver
supplies to a shop.

*Driving a truck could
be fun*, thinks Carl.

Next, Carl delivers a car to the construction site. A **cement mixer** is there. The body of the mixer is always turning so that the cement does not harden. *Driving a cement mixer could be fun,* thinks Carl. Everyone stops working to look at the new car that Carl delivered. The workers tell Carl that he is lucky because he gets to deliver new cars to people.

Back at the car depot, Carl loads his transporter with more cars. It looks like another busy day tomorrow. But Carl doesn't mind. *Driving a car transporter is fun,* thinks Carl.

# Building a Road
## Game

Different trucks and diggers are needed to build a road. Who will finish first?

**This fun road game is for 2 to 4 players.**

First, find a small plastic toy for each player. Place each toy on the start line, then roll a dice to see who goes first. The player who rolls the highest number goes first. Take turns moving along the road, counting as you go. Follow the instructions on the signs that you land on. The first person to finish building the road wins!

**START**

9

10

Dump load in the wrong spot. Lose a turn!

**FINISH**

Hooray! The road is finished. You win!

1

2

**3** Stop to unload a lorry. Lose a turn!

4

8

**7** Cement truck is late. Go back 3 places.

6

**5** Fill up dumper. Take an extra turn!

11

**12** Finish painting lines on road. Go forward three places.

13

14

18

17

**16** Use digger to speed up job. Take an extra turn!

15

# A Bedtime Story:
## Tommy's Party

Tommy couldn't wait for his birthday to arrive. He was going to have a truck party! His mum offered to make a birthday cake that looked just like a truck. It would be covered with red and yellow icing, and it would have chocolate biscuits for wheels, jellybeans for lights, licorice strips for the grill, and a trailer full of sweets.

But best of all, Tommy's dad was a lorry driver, and he had agreed to let all Tommy's friends have a ride in his big, red truck!

When the big day arrived, it was raining hard. Tommy's dad came into Tommy's bedroom very early to say happy birthday. He had to go to the building site to make a delivery but promised to be home in plenty of time for the party.

Tommy had a very busy morning helping his mum make the truck cake (and licking the bowl and spoon) and collecting his birthday post. Pretty soon, his friends arrived. Tommy got lots of truck presents from his friends. Julie gave him a book filled with pictures of trucks, and Bruce gave him a truck pen set. Tommy thanked his friends and told them that, as a special treat, his dad would let them all have rides in his truck. But wait a minute. Where was Tommy's dad?

At the building site, Tommy's dad had a problem. It had been raining hard all morning, and the building site was covered in deep, sticky mud. The truck was stuck! Tommy's dad had been trying to get the truck out of the mud. He gritted his teeth, gripped the steering wheel and put his foot down hard on the accelerator. The engine let out a loud, *vroooooooooom*! But still no luck! The big, red truck was stuck!

What was he going to do? Tommy was counting on him to bring his truck to the party. But just then, out of the corner of his eye, Tommy's dad saw something. The bulldozer on the building site had also got stuck in the mud, and a huge recovery truck had just arrived to tow it out. Quickly, Tommy's dad jumped out of the cab of his truck and ran over to where the recovery truck had pulled up.

Tommy's dad waved his arms at the driver. "Please, before you tow the bulldozer, can you tow my truck out of the mud? I promised my son that I would come to his birthday party!" he shouted.

"It would be my pleasure," said the driver, and drove the recovery truck over to where Tommy's dad's truck was stuck.

The recovery truck driver attached a steel cord to the front of Tommy's dad's truck. "Now, get behind the wheel of your truck. On the count of three, get ready to steer," said the driver as he revved his powerful engine. Tommy's dad did as he was told. "Ready? Okay. 1 … 2 … 3!" called the recovery truck driver …

Back at home, Tommy was just about to tell his friends that the truck rides weren't going to happen after all when, from outside, there came the sound of a truck's deep *tooooooooot!* Tommy's friends rushed to the window to see. And there, coming up the street, was Tommy's dad's truck. Tommy's friends all cheered.

"Now we can have rides in Dad's big, red truck!" said Tommy proudly. And they did … followed by enormous pieces of Mum's truck cake.

# Can You Count?:
## How Many Diggers?

**How many diggers are there in each line?**

Can you count them?

Which line has the most diggers in it? Which line has the least?

# Number words

One

Two

Three

Four

Five

Six

Can you match the number words to the right numbers of vehicles?
Use the colour codes to help you.

# Can You Count?:
## Load the Trucks

## Can you help to load the trucks?

Look at these two trucks. They are both the same but they have different loads. Which one will be quicker to load?

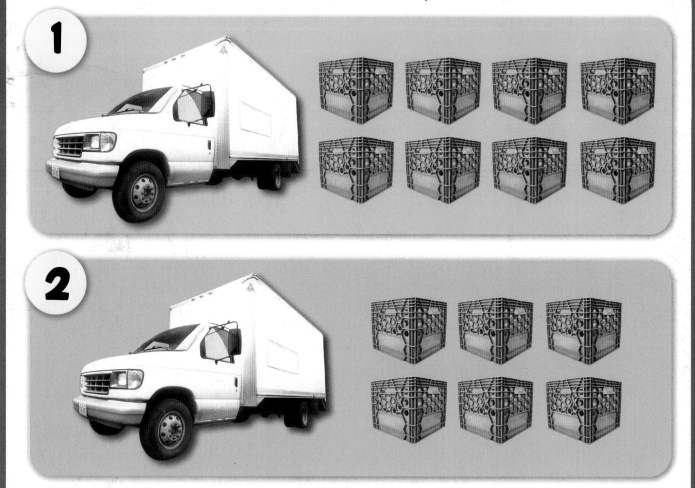

How many crates does Truck 1 have to load?

How many crates does Truck 2 have to load?

# Can you match each load to the right truck?

Use the colour clues to help you.

Which truck do you think will finish loading first?

Which truck has six things in it?

# Spot the Difference

**Truck and digger drivers need to be alert when using their vehicles.** They need to be able to spot when something is wrong.

Look at these two pictures.
Can you spot the four differences between them?

**Answers: 1.** The digger has changed from yellow to red. **2.** The arm on the back of the digger is missing. **3.** The load from the dump truck is missing. **4.** The back of the dump truck has changed from yellow to green.

# Make a
# Digger

**Follow these instructions to make your own digger.**
You will need an adult to help you.

**You will need:** **1.** a big shoe box **2.** tubes from two paper towel rolls **3.** a smaller box (without a lid) **4.** plastic bottle tops **5.** glue and scissors **6.** paints and paintbrush

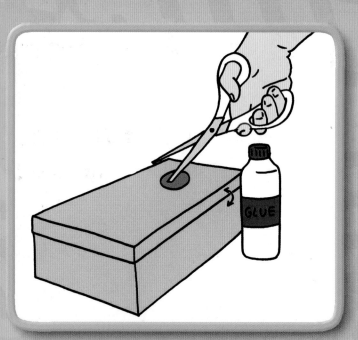

**1.** Draw a circle at one end of the lid of the shoe box by tracing around the end of the paper towel tube. Ask an adult to cut out the hole as shown. Then, glue the lid onto the shoe box.

**2.** Next, ask the adult to make a hole at the end of one of the tubes as shown.

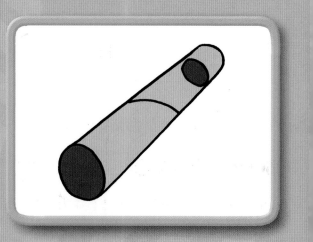

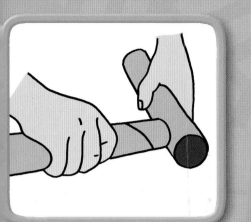

**3.** Push the second tube through the hole in the first tube to make an L shape. Use glue to hold the tubes together if needed. (You may need an adult to help you.)

**4.** Glue the inside of the smaller box to the end of the second tube as shown. Push the digger's L-shaped arm through the hole in the shoe box lid as shown. The L-shaped arm should lean on an angle.

**5.** Glue the plastic bottle tops on each side of the shoe box to make the wheels. Now you can paint your digger. Look at the pictures in this book to see which colours to use.

**You should be able to put small loads into the scoop of your digger.** What happens if you put some gravel into the scoop?

# Word Finder

**Here are some of the words used in this book.** Can you remember what they mean? Go back and look through the book to see if you can find each word again.

truck    petrol    earth

digger    tractor    tyre

grill    tracks    grain

snow    bulldozer    hay

red    cement    farmer

arms    bucket    blue

lights    plough    cab